Is this Bangers or Mash?

1

It's Bangers. He is big.
He has a red hat on.

2

Bangers gets an egg
from the box on the table.

He puts the egg
in his hat.

It's fun to throw the egg
and catch it.

Bangers throws the egg up
1 . . .2 . . . 3 times.

Mash runs in.
He has no hat on.

He runs into Bangers.

Can you see the egg?
Will it hit Mash?

It **did**!
Bang on top of his head!

Mash cries
as egg runs in his eyes.

Mum runs in.
She rubs the egg off.

12

She is cross with Bangers.
She tells him off.

But she gives Mash
a big hug.

Bangers cries. He has
to have a hug as well.

Then they have eggs
for tea.